The Little B
of P

Ideas for phonic activities for
the foundation stage

by Sally Featherstone

Illustrations by
Liz Persse

AaBbCc

The Little Book of Phonics

ISBN 1-902233-67-0

First published August 2001
Reprinted February 2002

Published in the United Kingdom by
Featherstone Education Ltd
44 - 46 High Street
Husbands Bosworth
Leicestershire   LE17 6LP
tel: +44 (0)185 888 1212   fax: +44 (0)185 888 1360

Introduction

Practitioners in the Foundation Stage have often said that the teaching of phonics to very young children needs an **active setting**. **OFSTED inspectors and LEA advisers say** that children are too often being asked to complete worksheets and complete sedentary tasks in connection with the teaching of phonics.

We all know that **children learn best by doing, making, singing, exploring** - preferably using all their senses and their whole bodies, and with familiar, natural materials. It is also now thought that children learn the principles of phonics more quickly by introducing **more than one sound each week**, so you visit each sound more frequently. It is also suggested that you group letters according to their shape, their sound or their characteristics.

(We have followed alphabetical order in the book to enable you to find your way around easily - we do not suggest that you must follow alphabetical order!)

The 'Treasure Basket'

In this book, we have incorporated the notion of a **'Treasure Basket'** for each letter - a collection of objects for each sound - natural and man made, familiar or less so, enabling children to explore the features of the objects while learning their names and initial sounds. If you collect your own phonic baskets, the contents of each one can be stored in a bag or box between uses, making it easier to return to the sound for reinforcement.

Of course, you could have two (or more) baskets in use at any time, particularly as the children get older and more confident. The baskets can then provide a phonic sorting activity, encouraging children to vocalise and extend both their phonic knowledge and their vocabulary.

Surrounding the basket illustration for each letter is a **selection of words** you might use in phonic activities, games, etc.

3

The right hand page in each pair gives **ideas for further phonic activities** to use throughout the day and week, using the sound(s) of the week in other regular activities such as songs, stories, snacks, cooking, movement, construction and art. We are sure you will add to the activities over time, using your own ideas.

We are not suggesting that you should use all the ideas, or that this is an exhaustive list! We are hoping that you will be able to use some ideas to extend phonics from a paper and pencil activity into the life of your classroom and involve children in enjoyable phonics sessions with a sense of fun.   .

What are they learning?

The **Early Learning Goals** connected with these activities are:

* extend their vocabulary, exploring the meanings and sounds of new words
* hear and say initial sounds in words
* link sounds to letters, naming and sounding the letters of the alphabet
* explore and experiment with sounds
* use their phonic knowledge to write simple regular words and make phonetically plausible attempts at more complex words
* write their own names and other things such as labels and captions

We would also add these intentions:

* learn that phonics are fun
* learn through real life experiences and objects
* learn using their whole bodies and all of their senses

The Little Book of Phonics

At the bottom of each right hand page, we have included the relevant **high frequency words** from the Literacy Strategy for Reception.

We have also included some ideas for **songs, rhymes and stories**. Those marked * can be found in 'This Little Puffin', ISBN 0-14-034048-3

Additional resources

The phonic basket illustrations for each letter of the alphabet are also available as A4 enlargements to use as discussion pictures, display posters or for individual children to use to as clues to their own collections of pictures, objects or words.

Tel: 01858 881212 for details

Contents

Page focus   **page**

Introduction   pages 3 & 4

Alphabetically ordered pages with
treasure baskets and activities   8 to 59

(Th and Sh pages follow s and t)

Listening games   60 & 61

acrobat
actor
address
album
alligator
almond
alphabet
alsatian
ambulance
animal
ankle
ant
anorak
antlers
apple
arch
arm
armadillo
armchair
artist

asparagus
asthma
astronaut
athlete
atlas
aquarium
avocado
axe

Ayesha
Ann
Anna
Andrew

ABC
ace
ache
acorn
alien
angel
ape
apricot
apron
aeroplane
aerosol
aerial
aerobics

names
Abdul
Adam
Agnes
Alan
Alex
Ali
Asha

special words
April
August
Autumn
America
Africa
Asia
Australia

smell

apricots
apples
avocado

hear

animals

taste & snack

avocado
apple
asparagus
anchovy
aniseed
almond

cook

apple pie,
apricot slices

be

actors
acrobats
archers
astronauts
airmen
drive an
ambulance

explore

aquariums
arches
atlases

make

an airport
an aquarium
an ant farm
aeroplanes
animal masks

move your body

arms &
ankles

song & story

Apple songs; ABC; Aiken Drum;
Aeroplanes All in a Row*;
Animal Fair*

can you?

aim
answer
be asleep
be awake

agree
add
be afraid
be angry

HFWords

and
at
are
away

all
a
am

*This Little Puffin ISBN 0-14-034048-3

9

baby
badge
bag
ball
ballerina
balloon
banana
bandage
bandana
bangle
banjo
bark
baseball
basin
bat
bath
bauble
beach
beads
bear

bed
bell
belt
bhaji
bib
bike
bikini

bingo
binoculars
bird
birthday
biscuit
blanket
blossom
block

boat
book
bottle
bow
bowl
box
boy

bracelet
brick
bride
bridge
brooch
broom
brush

bucket
budgie
bulldozer
bunk beds
burger
bus
butterfly
button

Bb

names

Barry
Bruce
Barbara

special words

Britain
Bangladesh
Belgium

colours

blue
brown
black

smell
berries
beans
bananas
bread

hear
bells
birds

taste & snack
bananas
beans
biscuits
bacon
blackberries
blueberries

cook
bread
biscuits
beans on toast
bhajis
black beans
buns

be
bears
brides
babies
ballerinas
Batman
Bob the Builder

explore
beetles
babies
bubbles
blackboards

make
buildings
bridges
boats
balloon prints
a beach

move your body
back
body
bones

song & story
3 Bears; Baby's Catalogue; Its the Bear!; Baa Baa Black Sheep; Bobby Shaftoe; Bye Baby Bunting; Bananas in Pyjamas; Baby Peter*; Birthday Candles*; Bread and Jam*

can you?
bark
blink
behave
bend
build
buzz
breathe
balance
bang
blow
bite
bounce
boogie

HFWords
big

*This Little Puffin ISBN 0-14-034048-3

cactus   cat   confetti   cracker
cage   catalogue   conker   crayon
cake   caterpillar coconut   cream
calculator cauliflower coins   crisps
calendar   clipboard   colander   crocodile
calf   cloak   cone   crown
camera   clock   cook   cup
can   clogs   cork   cutter
canary   cloud   cuckoo
candle
canoe   <u>names</u>
cap   Cameron
cape   Carly
car   Chris

caravan   coach   corn   <u>special words</u>
card   coat   cornflakes Caribbean
cardboard   coal   cot   Cornwall
cardigan   comb   cotton wool <u>colours</u>
carpet   combine   counter   cream
carrier   comic   cow
carrot   compass   cowboy
cartoon   concertina crab

12

smell

coffee   cloves
coriander
curry   cumin

hear

cats   cars
canaries

taste & snack

carrots
cake
cookies
coconut
corn
crisps

cook

cup cakes
custard
coconut cakes
curry
crumble
chappatis

be

caterpillars
crocodiles
cats
cooks
crabs
cowboys

explore

compost
clay
cornflour
carbon paper
calculators
cash registers
colours

make

castles
crowns
clothes lines
constructions
costumes
curls

move your body

creep & crawl
cross legs
curl

song & story

La Cuccaracha;   Cuckoo;
Chick, Chick Chicken;
Chapatti in your Hand*;
Cows in the Kitchen*;
Curry and Rice*

can you?

call
carry
catch
clap
clean

click
colour
comb
cook
curtsy

cut
cough
count
click
cry

HFWords

cat
come
can

*This Little Puffin ISBN 0-14-034048-3

dad
daffodil
daisy
dancer
dandelion
deckchair
deer
dentist
deodorant
desert
desk
dessert
detergent
dog
dinosaur
dice
diamond
diary
dictionary
digger
dish
dishcloth

dishwasher
disinfectant
diver
doctor
dome
donkey
door
doorknob
dormouse
doughnut
dove
dragon
dragonfly
dress
drawing
drawing
pin
drink
drum
duck

dustpan
duvet
Duplo

Damian
Darren
Davina
Dawn

Denmark
Diwali
December

dark blue

smell
disinfectant
dog biscuits
hear
dogs
doves
diggers

taste & snack
dates
doughnuts
damson jam
dried fruit

cook
dumplings
doughnuts
dinosaur
  biscuits
dough
dropscones

be
dinosaurs
dentists
dancers
divers
disc jockeys
disco dancers
drummers

explore
the dark
digging
docks and dams
dough and dye
ducks in water
dominoes
draughts

make
drawings
deserts
dinosaurs
Duplo models
dough

move your body
drag
dive
disco dance

song & story
Dogger; Dinosaur Roar; 7 Dwarfs;
Daisy, Daisy; Down by the Station;
Daisy the Duck; 5 Little Ducks
went Swimming One Day;
Diwali is Here*

can you?
dance
deliver
dial
dig

disco dance
divide
dive
doodle
draw

doze
drink
dress
dust
drum

HFWords
dog
dad
day

*This Little Puffin ISBN 0-14-034048-3

15

ear
elephant
eagle
earphones
earring
earwig
Easter egg
egg
eel
egg cup
elastic
electric
elf
emergency
envelope
Eskimo
exit
eye
eyebrow
eyelid
eyelash
excavator

engine
explorer

Easter
Eid
England

Eamon
Edward
Eileen
Elliott
Elroy
Elvis
Emily
Eric
Ewan

emerald

smell

hear

elephants
emergency bells
and sirens

taste & snack

eggs
egg sandwiches
Edam cheese

cook

boiled eggs
egg custard
egg sandwiches

be

elephants
eggs hatching
elves

explore

eggshells
excavation
emptying
elastic

make

painted eggs
elephants
earrings

move your body

ears
eyes
elbows

song & story

Elmer the Patchwork Elephant;
The Elephant and the Bad Baby;
The Elves & the Shoemaker;
Echo*; Eggs and Bacon*

can you?

eat
empty
erase
escape

examine
experiment
explain
explode

HFWords

*This Little Puffin ISBN 0-14-034048-3

17

fabric five saucer frilly
fact fire foam frock
fairground fireman food frogman
fairy fire foot frying pan
family engine footstep funnel
fan firework fork furniture
fancy fizzy forest
dress flag
farm

names
Fred
Freda
Frances
Fiona

feather
fish
fisherman fly fountain
flat frog fox
food flower foxglove
fence flies frame
fern flannel freezer
ferry flowerpot freckles
friends flying fridge

special words
France

colours
fawn

18

smell

fabric softener

fruit

flowers

hear

fluttering   flies

taste & snack

fruit

figs

fruit cake

fruit salad

fig rolls

cook

fairy cakes

flapjack

fruit buns

fruit salad

fudge

be

feathers

falling

farmers

fishermen

fish

frogs

explore

feathers

freezing

fur & fabric

filling

favourites

fruits

furniture

make

foam prints

fabric pictures

farms & fences

finger and

footprints

flags

move your body

fall

float

follow my leader

song & story

Five Little Speckled Frogs;
Farm animals; Five Fat Fish;
The Farmer's in his Den;
Little Rabbit Frou Frou;
Five Songs*; Michael Finnigan*

can you?

fall
faint
fan
fetch
fasten

fill
fish
fix
flap
flick

flop
fly
fold
freeze
frown

HFWords

for

*This Little Puffin ISBN 0-14-034048-3

goose
goalkeeper
garden
garage
gate
gears
ghost
gift
girl
glass
glasses
globe
glove
glue
goat
goldfish
gooseberry
gorilla
grandma
grandad
grape
grapefruit

grass
grasshopper
greenhouse
greyhound
guinea pig
guitar

giant
gerbil
geranium
gymnastics

Gerry
Gary
Gloria
Gordon
Gracie

Gg

Germany
Ghana

green
grey
gold

smell

garlic
garam masala
ginger
grass

hear

ghosts, giggles

taste & snack

grapes
green jelly
guava
ginger
grapefruit

cook

garlic bread
green jelly
gingerbread

be

grandmas
and grandads
goalies
giants
ghosts

explore

gloop
green
gardens
glue

make

a garage
a garden

move your body

gallop

song & story

Mr Gumpy; Gobbolino;
Goosey, Goosey Gander;
Granny in the Kitchen*;
Grandmother's Footsteps

can you?

gaze
giggle
give
glare

glue
gossip
grin
grip

greet
groan
grumble

HFWords

go
going
get

*This Little Puffin ISBN 0-14-034048-3

hat
hamster
hedgehog
hair
handbag
hoop
hairband
hairbrush
hairslide
hawk
helicopter
halo
half
hamburger
hamper
handcuffs
handkerchief
hang glider
harbour
harmonica
harp
haystack

head-dress
head teacher
headphones
hedge
helmet

helter skelter
hemisphere
hexagon
hippopotamus
hive
hole
horse
house

horn
hose
hospital
hot water
  bottle
hovercraft
humming-
  bird
hyacinth
hundred

<u>names</u>

Hannah
Henry
Hugh
Harriet

<u>special words</u>

Holland

<u>colours</u>

heliotrope

smell

hand cream

herbs

hear

humming

harmonica

taste & snack

herbs

honey

hot dogs

healthy food

hummus

cook

honey cakes

herby bread

hot cross buns

hot dogs

be

hairdressers

hunters

hummingbirds

horses

explore

hard

heavy

hot

homes

hundreds

make

houses

hand prints

harbours

hats

move your body

hop

hip hop

song & story

Harry the Dirty Dog; Hickory Dickory, Hive for a Honey Bee; Happy Birthday; Hello Peter*; Higgledy Piggledy*; Humpty Dumpty*; Heads & Shoulders*

can you?

hang

heap

hear

help

hiccup

hiss

hit

hop

hold

hoot

hug

hum

hurry

hypnotise

HFWords

he

*This Little Puffin ISBN 0-14-034048-3

23

igloo
imp
ill
illustration
imagine
inch
indoors
infant
infectious
insect
initials
ink
inside
inspector
instruction
invalid
invitation

ice cream
ice lolly
icicle
iron
iris
island
ivy

names

Ian
Imelda
Isaac

special words

India
Ireland
Italy

colours

indigo

smell

incense

hear

ice cream van

taste & snack

ice cubes
ice cream

cook

ice cream cake
ice lollies
icing

be

inspectors
ice cream
      sellers
inventors
imps

explore

ice
islands
inside

make

ink blots
igloos

move your body

inch
incline
itch

song & story

In and Out the Dusty Bluebells*;
In a Cottage in a Wood*;
Incy Wincy Spider*

can you?

illustrate
inflate
interfere
interrupt

introduce
invite
iron
irritate

invent
ignore
imitate
interview

HFWords

I
is
in
it

*This Little Puffin ISBN 0-14-034048-3

25

jam
jack in a box
joker
jaguar
jackdaw
jacket
jar
jeans
jelly
jellybeans
jellyfish
jeep
jersey
jet
jewel
jigsaw
jockey
jungle
judo
jug

jumpsuit
junk
jumper

jack
Jade
Jatinder
Jill
Joan
John
Jonie
Jeremy
Judy
Julie

Japan
January
July
June

jade

smell
jam and jelly
juice

hear
jokes
jingles

taste & snack
jam
jelly
juice
Jaffas

cook
jam tarts
jacket potatoes
jelly

be
jack in a box
jumpers
jellyfish

explore
jungles
junk
jewels

make
jigsaws
junk models

move your body
jump
jog and jiggle
jazz dance

song & story
The Jigaree; Mr and Mrs Jump
the Jockeys; Jingle Bells;
Jack and Jill; Jelly on a Plate*;
John Brown*; Three Jellyfish*

Can you
jab
jig
jiggle
jog
joke
juggle
jump

HFWords

*This Little Puffin ISBN 0-14-034048-3

kagoul
kaleidoscope
kangaroo
karaoke
kayak
kebab
kennel
ketchup
kettle
kerb
key
keyhole
keyboard
kid
kilt
king
kingfisher
kiss
kitchen
kiwi fruit
kiwi
koala

kung fu
Kit-Kat
kite
kitten

knife
knee
knob
knock
knocker
knickers
knit
knot

names

Kate
Kamal
Ken

special words

Kenya

colours

khaki

28

smell

ketchup

hear

kettles

kittens

taste & snack

kiwi fruit

ketchup

cook

fruit kebabs

be

kind

kings

kangaroos

koalas

explore

keys and locks

kites

kaleidoscopes

make

kaleidoscopes

kitchens

kites

move your body

kick

song & story

Katie Morag;

Knock at the Door*;

King of the Castle

can you?

kick

keep

be kind

kiss

kneel

knock

sing karaoke

HFWords

*This Little Puffin ISBN 0-14-034048-3

label
ladybird
lace
laces
ladder
ladle
lady
lamb
lamp
lampshade
lantern
lavatory
lawn
lawn mower
lead
leaf
leaflet
Lego
lemon
lemonade
lens
leopard

letter box
library
lifeboat
light
lighthouse
lightning
lily
lilac

lime
limpet
line
list
lion
lipstick
liquorice

list
lizard
llama
loaf
lobster
lock
log
lollipop
lorry
lottery
loudspeaker
lunch

names

Leo
Louise
Lucy

special words

London

colours

lime
lemon

smell

lime
lemon
lavender

hear

lullabies

taste & snack

letter biscuits
lasagne
lentils
lollies
liquorice
lemon curd

cook

alphabet pasta
lemonade
letter biscuits

be

letter writers
limbo dancers
lion tamers

explore

letters
light
long & large
life in a lawn
liquids
ladders
lines

make

labels
letters
lists
leaf prints
line patterns,
letter boxes

move your body

limbo dancing
line dancing
legs and lips

song & story

The Bad Tempered Ladybird;
Ladybird L adybird;*
Oranges and Lemons;
Little Arabella Miller*;
Looby Loo*

can you?

lace
lie down
limp
lasso

laugh
laze
learn
leave
lick

lift
listen
look
lose

HFWords

look
like

*This Little Puffin ISBN 0-14-034048-3

macaroni
machine
mackintosh
magazine
magnet
magnifying
 glass
magpie
make-up
man
mango
map
marble
marigold
marmalade
marzipan
mat
material
maze
maypole
measles
medal

melon
meringue
mermaid
merry go
 round
motorbike
motorway
mountain

Mm

mousse
mouse
mouth
organ
mud
mug

microphone
microwave
milk
mill
mince pie
miner
mirror
mint
mittens

mobile
 phone
model
mole
money
monster
moon
mop

moth
mother
Mum
mushroom
music

Martin
Mary
Marianne
Meena
Megan
Mahalia

March
May

mauve
maroon
mustard

smell

mint mango
Marmite
mustard

hear

motors music

taste & snack

marmalade
marshmallow
mango
melon
milk
marzipan

cook

milk puddings
meringues
mince pies
macaroons
mousse
marmalade

be

Mums
magicians
miners
milkmen
mechanics
messengers

explore

mud
magnets
mirrors
magnifying
    glasses

make

marks
mazes
menus
mobiles
models

move your body

mouth music
march

song & story

Miss Polly; Mousie, Mousie*;
Mystery Man*; Mog;
Meg and Mog;
The Muffin Man

can you?

make
mail
put on makeup
mark

match
march
mend
meet
mess
miaow

mop
moo
move
munch

HFWords

my
mum
me

*This Little Puffin ISBN 0-14-034048-3

nail
name
naan
nanny
nag
nap
napkin
narrow
nasturtium
naughty
navy
neck
necklace
nectarine
needle
nephew
nerves
nest
net
nettle

newspaper
newt
nibble
nice
niece
night
nightie
nightmare
nine
no
nod
noise
noodle
nose

nosy
nostril
note
notice
number
nun
nurse
nursery
nut
nutcrackers
nutmeg
nylon

names
Nancy
Nathan
Narinder
Nazreem
Ned
Noah
Noreen
Norman

special words
November
Norway

colours
navy blue

smell

nutmeg

hear

noises

taste & snack

nectarines
noodles
nougat
nuts

cook

noodles
naan bread

be

nuns
nurses
newts
newsagents
newsreaders

explore

noise makers
numbers
newspaper

make

notices
notes
noises
newspapers

move your body

nod
nose
neck

song & story

Alex's New Clothes;
The Last Noonoo;
noisy stories like Peace at Last;
I had a Little Nut Tree

can you?

neigh
nod
nag
nestle

nibble

HFWords

no

*This Little Puffin ISBN 0-14-034048-3

oak
oats
oblong
oboe
octagon
octopus
off
office
officer
ogre
oil
ointment
olive
old
omelette
on
opera
orange
orangeade
orang-utan
orchard
orbit

ostrich
oven
over
oxygen

open
oval
overcoat
ocean
owl

Oscar
Ossie

October

orange
olive

36

smell

oregano
onion

hear

owls

taste & snack

omelette
orange
orange juice
olives
onions

cook

omelette
oatcakes
onions

be

octopuses
opera singers
officers
opticians
orang-utans

explore

openings
order
oblongs
ovals
octagons

make

orange pictures

move your body

over things

song & story

Owls;
Ostriches;
Wide Eyed Owl*
Old MacDonald Had a Farm

can you?

open
be old
go over

HFWords

on
of

*This Little Puffin ISBN 0-14-034048-3

packet   parrot   penguin   play
pad   parsley   penny   plum
paddle   parsnip   perfume   poem
padlock   party   person   police
page   pasta   pet   pond
pagoda   paste   petrol   present
pain   path   piano   princess
paint   pattern   picture   prince
paintbrush pea   puppet
palace   puppy
palm tree   pushchair
pan   puzzle

pancake

panda

pansy   peacock   pie   Peter
panto   peanut   pig   Paul
pants   pear   pine cone   Pushba
paper   pebble   pip

parachute   pedal   pixie   Pakistan
parade   peg   pizza

parasol   pelican   plane   purple
park   pencil   plate   pink

smell

peppermint
perfumed oils
parsley

hear

people
popcorn pop

taste & snack

pear
parsnip
pumpkin
pineapple
plums
passion fruit
papaya

cook

pizza & pasta
pitta bread
pancakes
popcorn
porridge
pastry

be

postmen
pop singers
puppeteers
painters
pianists

explore

pastry
playdough
puppets
paint

make

paint pictures
use pasta
paper chains
portraits

move your body

pull and push

song & story

The Big Pancake; Peepo; Pingu;
Polar bear stories;
Where is the Green Parrot?;
Pitter Patter Raindrops; Peter
Piper; Miss Polly; Mix a Pancake

can you?

pull	paint	point
push	play	pat
puff	peep	patter
pop	poke	press

HFWords

play

*This Little Puffin ISBN 0-14-034048-3

Queenie
Quentin

quack
quads
quarter
queen
question
quiche
quick
quiet
quilt
quince
quins
quiz
quoit

special words

colours

40

smell
quince

hear
questions

taste & snack
everything in
quarters

cook
quiche

be
quads
quins
queens
quiet

explore
quiet places
quick movers
questions

make
quilts
quill pens

move your body
quickly and
quietly

song & story
The Baked Bean Queen;
The Patchwork Quilt;
Granny's Quilt

can you?
quack
quiver
be quick
be quiet

HFWords

*This Little Puffin ISBN 0-14-034048-3

rabbit	rest	room	names
race	rhino	root	Ramesh
radiator	rhubarb	rope	Ravi
radio	rhyme	rose	Richard
radish	ribbon	round	Rita
raffle	ride	rucksack	Robert
raft	ring		Rose
railway			Roy
rain			Rudy
rainbow			Rupa
raisin			
rake			
raspberry			
rat			

Rr

special words

Rama
Ramadan
Rastafarian

rattle	river	rug
read	road	ruler
record	roof	run
reception		
recycle		
reggae		
register		
reptile		

colours

red
rose

smell
raspberries
roses
rosemary

hear
radio
reggae

taste & snack
raspberries
red food
raisins
rice
rice cakes

cook
rhubarb
rice
ravioli

be
readers
roadmakers
ringmasters
rabbits
racehorses

explore
red
recorders
radio
rope
rough things
ribbons on sticks

make
ribbon pictures
round pictures
rockets

move your body
run
roll

song & story
Rosie's Walk;
Robert the Rose Horse;
Red Riding Hood; Ruby;
Ring a Roses*;
Round and Round the Garden*

can you?
race
reply
roar
roll
rub
run
rush

HFWords

*This Little Puffin ISBN 0-14-034048-3

43

sack	sequin	sleeve	soldier
safety pin	settee	slice	soup
sailor	silly	slide	spaceship
salad	sing	slipper	spider
samosa	sink	slow	splash
sand	sister	smack	sponge
sandal			spoon
sandwich			square
satchel			stamp
saucepan			stone
sausage			strawberry
saw		smell	summer
scales	sit	smile	sun
scarf	six	smoke	sweet
school	skate	snack	

Ss

scissors	skin	snail	
scooter	skip	snake	
sea	skirt	snow	
seagull	skittle	snowdrop	
seaside	sky	soap	
seed	sledge	soccer	
see-saw	sleep	sock	

special words

Saturday
Sunday
Scotland
Spain

colours

scarlet
silver

smell
spices
strawberries
sardines

hear
sounds of
summer

taste & snack
sweetcorn
strawberries
samosas
sorbet
soy sauce
syrup

cook
sandwiches
soup
samosas
shortbread
sponge
scones

be
spacemen
school teachers
soccer players
snails

explore
seeds
sequins
sponges
string
soap bubbles
sunlight

make
seasides
supermarkets
spaceships
sponge prints

move your body
stand and sit
slide and slip
play sardines

song & story
Seven Fat Sausages; Simon Says; Simple Simon; A Sailor went to Sea, Sea, Sea *; Sally go Round the Sun*; Skip to my Lou*; Sing a Song of Sixpence*

can you?
sit
scream
scratch
scribble
scrub
sing
skid
skip
slap
slip
smile
sniff
snore
speak
sprinkle

HFWords
said
see

*This Little Puffin ISBN 0-14-034048-3

45

shadow	✻shop	
shake	short	Sharon
✻shampoo	shorts	Shawn
sharp	shoulder	Shirley
shawl	shout	Shane
shed	show	Shula
✗sheep	shower	
sheepdog	shrink	
shed	shut	
sheet	shy	
sheikh		
shelf		
✻shell		
sherrif		
shield		
shiny		
ship		
shirt		
✻shoe		
shoelace		
shoo!		
shoot		

Sh sh

smell
shampoo
shaving cream

hear
shouting

taste & snack
sherbert
sherbert
lemons

cook
shortbread
shish-kebabs

be
shopkeepers in
a shoe shop

explore
shadows
shiny things
shells

make
shadow puppets
shakers

move your body
shoulders
shrug

song & story
Shirley's Shops;
The Snowman;
She'll be Coming Round the
Mountain*

can you?
shout
shoot
shrug
show

HFWords
she

*This Little Puffin ISBN 0-14-034048-3

table	telephone	tightrope	tooth
tablecloth	telescope	tights	toothbrush
tablet	television	till	top
tadpole	temple	time	torch
tail	ten	tinsel	tortoise
takeaway	tennis	tiny	towel
tall	tent	tissue	toy
tambourine	terrapin	toad	tractor
tank			train
tap			trainers
tarantula			trapeze
target			tray
tart			treasure
tattoo		toadstool	tree
taxi	terrier	toast	triangle
tea	terrify	toddler	tricycle
teacher	test	toffee	trousers
teapot	ticket	toilet	truck
team	tiddler	tomato	trumpet
teaspoon	tidy	tongue	twins
teddy	tie	tonsils	special words
teeth	tiger	tool	Tuesday

48

smell
toast
tea

hear
tractors
trains
trumpets

taste & snack
turnip
toast
tomatoes
tangerines
tortilla chips

cook
toast
tagliatelle
toasted
   teacakes
treacle tart
trifle

be
trains
toddlers
trumpeters
trapeze artists
tarantulas
toys

explore
timber
towelling
tinsel
telescopes
telephones
towers

make
towers
telescopes
trains
tracks
trails
tents

move your body
teeth
tongue

song & story
Titch; Ten little Teddies;
The EnormousTurnip; Ten in a Bed;
Tambourine, Tambourine*;
Teddy Bear, Teddy Bear*;
Tommy Thumb*

can you?
talk
taste
tear
terrify
thank

tickle
tiptoe
toss
touch
trace

tremble
tumble
turn
twist

HFWords
to

*This Little Puffin ISBN 0-14-034048-3

thank	thing	throw
theatre	third	thrush
thatch	thistle	thumb
theme park	thorn	thump
thermometer	through	thunder
thermos	thousand	

thick	thread	
thief	three	*special words*
thigh	throat	Thursday
thimble	throne	*names*
thin	through	Theo
		Thelma

smell

hear
thank you

taste & snack
thick shakes
hundreds &
    thousands

cook

be
visitors to a
theme park

explore
threading
thick & thin
thermometers

make
'thank you'
presents

move your body
slap your
  thighs
wave your
  thumbs

song & story
Thumbellina;
Tommy Thumb*

can you?
thank
think
thump

HFWords
the
they
this

*This Little Puffin ISBN 0-14-034048-3

51

Uu

Una
Ursula

special words

Urdu
Uganda

UFO   unpack
ugly   unplug
umbrella   unroll
unlock   unselfish
uncle   untie
under   until
underwear unwind
underground up
underpants uphill
underpass upstairs
understand urchin
undo
unfair
united
unkind

52

smell

hear

taste & snack

cook

be

Manchester United

explore

underground

make

move your body

go under and over

upside down

song & story

Under a Stone*;
Up the Hill*

can you?

undo

unroll

unwrap

unpack

unplug

HFWords

up

*This Little Puffin ISBN 0-14-034048-3

vaccination
vampire
vanilla
vase
vegetable
veil
vein
velvet
veranda
verse
vet
vicar
video
videotape
view
village
vinegar
violet
violin
visit
vixen
voice

vote
vowel
vulture

violet
viridian

Vv

Valerie
Vera
Veronica
Victoria
Vincent
Vladimir

smell

vinegar

vanilla

violets

hear

violins

taste & snack

vegetables

cook

vegetable
soup

be

vampires

van drivers

violinists

vicars

explore

velvet

vegetables

viewers

make

vegetable prints

verses

videos

move your body

very slowly

song & story

The Very Hungry Caterpillar;
Oliver's Vegetables

can you?

vote

HFWords

*This Little Puffin ISBN 0-14-034048-3

wagon
wafer
waistcoat
waiter
walk
wall
walking
stick
wallpaper
walnut
wand
wardrobe
warm
wash
washing
machine
wash up
wasp
watch
water
waterfall
wave

wear
weather
web
wedding
weed
weigh
wet
whale

Ww

wheelbarrow
wheelchair
whisker
whisper
whistle
wicked
wide
wife

wig
wigwam
wind
windmill
window
wing
witch
wizard
wood
woodpecker
wool
word
worm

names
Winston
Wendy

special words
Wednesday
Wales

colours
white

smell

washing powder
wood
wax

hear

water
waterfalls
wind chimes

taste & snack

wafers
walnuts
watermelon
watercress

cook

watercress
soup

be

witches
wizards
waiters
worms
woodpeckers

explore

water
washing
weather
wind

make

weavings
wind chimes
windmills
windsocks
wigwams

move your body

wiggle as you
walk
wave

song & story

Mrs Wobble the Waitress;
Mrs Wishy Washy; Willy the
Wimp; Wind the Bobbin*;
Worm at the Bottom of My
Garden*; Wheels on the Bus

can you?

waddle
walk
wake
wander

wash
watch
wave
weed
whisper

whistle
wiggle
wink
work

HF Words

we
went
was

*This Little Puffin ISBN 0-14-034048-3

57

X

x-ray
xylophone

Y

yacht
yam
yawn
yellow
yes
yodel
yoghurt
yolk
you
young
yo-yo

Z

zebra
zebra
  crossing
zero
zig-zag
zip
zoo
zoom

names

Xavier
Yvonne
Zak

colours

yellow

Xx Yy Zz

smell

hear

yells
zoo noises
xylophone

taste & snack

yoghurt
yams

cook

yellow jelly
yellow custard
yellow ice lollies

be

zoo keepers
zebras

explore

yellow things
yellow dough
x-rays

make

a zoo
zebra prints
zebra paintings
zebra crossings

move your body

zig-zag

song & story

Dear Zoo; Yankee Doodle*;
Yellow Butter*;
Yellow Submarine

can you?

yawn
yodel

zip
zoom
zig-zag

HFWords

you
yes

*This Little Puffin ISBN 0-14-034048-3

Listening Skills

In order to learn the different sounds, children need to improve and refine their listening skills and later, their visual discrimination. It is also vital to monitor children's hearing, as many suffer temporary hearing loss due to glue ear and allergies such as hay fever.

In the Foundation stage, games and activities which develop listening are both useful and important. Here are some old favourites, some with a new twist.

Chinese Whispers

Sit in a circle. The adult or a child thinks of an object and whispers it to the child on their left. this child whispers to the next one, and so on round the circle. When the word comes back to the starter, they say it out loud and see how near it is to what they said originally. (If the children are starting, it is a good idea if the adult sits on their left, in case the word is forgotten by the time it gets back!)

I Spy and I Hear

"I Spy with my little eye, something beginning with ----."
Vary this game by having a small collection of objects in the middle of the circle.

"I Hear with my little ear, something beginning with ----."

Describe it

Put a selection of objects from your sound basket on the floor. Describe one and see who can say the name. "I can see something that starts with 'b'. It is round and bouncy."

Then let the children describe an object. Make it more difficult by having objects from two baskets.

Listening Tapes

These can be made for indoors or out. If you can take photos of the things as you record them, you will help children who need a visual clue. Make these pictures into cards or a simple book by laminating the photos.

Find a Rhyme

This game is fun, and gets children listening to sounds. Encourage them to be inventive and make up words. Don't insist on 'real' words. Concentrate on listening and repeating the sound.

Start by saying "Can you make a rhyme with pat?" (eg cat, hat, rat, mat). "Can you make a rhyme with edge?" (eg veg, hedge, wedge, ledge)

Collections

Start with an empty basket and see how many things you can find starting with a chosen letter. If the thing is too big for the basket, draw a picture of it.

Sound Pictures

Look through magazines, catalogues and junk mail for pictures for a sound collection. take photos of objects in the room or outside. Make these into laminated cards for sorting or saying. Don't be tempted to put the letters on too early!

Listening Walks

Take a listening walk round your setting, the garden or the neighbourhood. Listen for the sounds. take photos or make a pictorial list of the things you see.

Musical Patterns

Play 'follow the leader' with clapping patterns or simple percussion beats. Use a drum or tambourine to beat out the rhythm of children's names, objects, words or poems.

If you have ideas for a little book - get in touch!

We often work in partnership with schools and individual teachers.

NOTES

NOTES